CAT KID
COMIC CLUB
ON PURPOSE

Tree-House Comix Proudly Presents

WORDS, ILLUSTRATIONS, AND ARTWORK BY

ALDI

■SCHOLASTIC

TO JEFF, JULIE, WILL, AND GRANT KINNEY

Published in the UK by Scholastic, 2023
1 London Bridge, London, SE1 9BG
Scholastic Ireland, 89E Lagan Road,
Dublin Industrial Estate, Glasnevin, Dublin, D11 HP5F

SCHOLASTIC and associated logos are trademarks
and/or registered trademarks of Scholastic Inc.

First published in the US by Scholastic Inc, 2022
First published in the UK by Scholastic Inc, 2022

Text and illustrations © Dav Pilkey, 2022

ISBN 978 0702 32540 3

A CIP catalogue record for this book is available from the British Library.

Printed by Bell & Bain, Glasgow
Paper made from wood grown in sustainable forests
and other controlled sources.

1 3 5 7 9 10 8 6 4 2

www.scholastic.co.uk

Illustrations, 3-D models, photography,
and hand lettering by Dav Pilkey.

All mini comics colored by Dav Pilkey using pencil, watercolors,
acrylic paints, markers, colored pencils, crayons, and gouache.
3-D models built out of recycled plastic lids, clay, paper, wood, wire,
tape, glue, broken toys, balloons, and other throwaway items.

Digital Color by Jose Garibaldi | Flatting by Aaron Polk
Editor: Ken Geist | Editorial Team: Megan Peace and Jonah Newman
Book design by Dav Pilkey and Phil Falco
Creative Director: Phil Falco
Publisher: David Saylor

CHAPTERS & COMICS

Find out who you are
and do it on purpose.

−Dolly Parton

Chapter 1

click
click
click

No.

Aw, maaaan!!!

Did she write back yet?

NO!

What's taking her so LONG???

Yeah! Where's MY MONEY AT???

I'm making a list of stuff I'm Gonna buy...

...when I become a **MillionAiRe!!!**

Let's see!

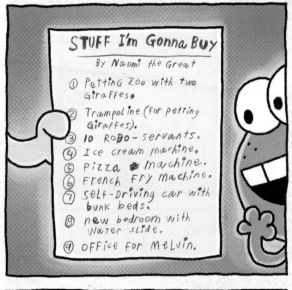

STUFF I'm Gonna Buy

By Naomi the Great

1. Petting zoo with two Giraffes.
2. Trampoline (for petting Giraffes).
3. 10 ROBO-servants.
4. Ice cream machine.
5. Pizza machine.
6. French Fry machine.
7. Self-Driving car with bunk beds.
8. New bedroom with water slide.
9. Office for Melvin.

Don't forget...

...I'm Your **AGENT...**

...So **I** get ten percent of whatever **YOU** Get!

Yeah, I know.

How do you expect to pay for all of this stuff?

When my book gets published...

...I'll be a **millionAiRe!**

Naomi, I don't think it's going to work like that.

WHY NOT?

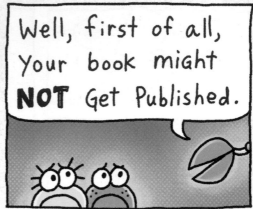

Well, first of all, your book might **NOT** get published.

We just sent it to the publisher **15** minutes ago!

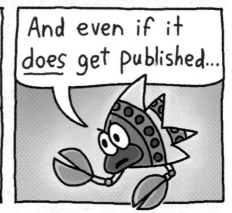

And even if it does get published...

...You probably **WON'T** make a **MILLION DOLLARS**...

... and even if you **DO**...

...I don't want you spending it all on silly things.

Any money you make...

...is going into the college fund!

COLLEGE?

That's like a hundred years from now!!!

What if I don't wanna go to college?

Then it can help pay for Melvin's college...

...and for anybody else who wants to Go!

FINE! I'LL GO TO COLLEGE!

If you don't STRAIGHTEN UP and FLY RIGHT...

...the only place YOU'LL be Going...

...is the TIME-OUT ROCK!

CHAPTER 2
Bedtime Worries

... You've got **60** Seconds to be **IN BED...**

... **UNDER The COVERS...**

... or it'll be **LIGHTS OUT...**

... with **NO READING!**

Why can't we have **ONE NIGHT** without...

What's wrong, Naomi?

Nothing.

Do you want to talk about it?

What if that lady never writes back?

I think she will.

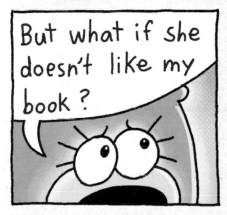

But what if she doesn't like my book?

That's okay!

Everybody doesn't have to like the same things.

I'm NEVER GONNA be RICH!

25

CHAPTER 3
The Big Surprise

The next day...

Hey, everybody...

Welcome back to the **THIRD** week of...

The **CAT KID COMIC CLUB!!!**

HOORAY!!!

28

Does Anybody Got a new Comic to share?

OH! OH! OH! OH! OH! OH!

Okay, Melvin.

My sister, **AND** my first client...

...Would like to share **HER** comic.

It's Gonna be **PUBLISHED!**

Melvin, we don't know that for sure.

The publisher still hasn't written back yet.

I know. But it's such a **GOOD BOOK**...

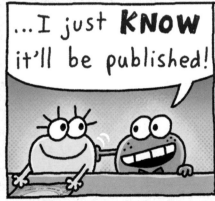

...I just **KNOW** it'll be published!

Show 'em, Naomi!

Okay!

Lou and Rose...

...would not wear clothes...

...but Grandma had a plan.

Underwear is fun to wear!!!

...and then the JOY BeGan!

But very soon, beneath the moon...

They came upon a siGht!

For down beLow, a fashion show...

Monster Fashion show

...had turned into a **FIGHT**!!!

Monster Fashion Show

"I am Dressed the VERY Best!"
Each Monster roared and Grumbled.

But Rose and Lou Knew what to do...

...to stop the monster Rumble.

Hand in hand...

...With dear old Gran...

...they Leaped onto the stage.

And Gave each foe a brand— **NEW** show...

...to end their senseless rage.

Vampire Joe looked down below

and found that it was true.

For under there was underwear with polka dots of blue.

MR. Hyde looked deep inside...

...then threw away his pants.

Look at these!
MY B.V.D.s...

...have baby
elephants!!!

"Check out mine,"
said Frankenstein.

They're pink with
little roses!!!

And the mummy's
drawers had
dinosaurs...

...to match her
pantyhoses.

39

And in the end,

they danced as friends...

...the biG ones and the small...

...Without a care, for underwear...

...Unites us one and all.

... is what is underneath!!!

THE END

About the Author / Illustrator

Naomi the Great

Naomi the Great is the world-renowned creator of <u>Monster Cheese Sandwich</u>.

When she is not making books, Naomi the Great enjoys reading, watching videos, and playing the drums.

That... was...

...AWESOME!!

Naomi's Gonna be a **MiLLiONAire!**

And She's Gonna buy us an **ICE-CreAM MAChine!**

I Said **"MAYbe"!**

We're still in negotiations.

44

No we don't.

Our friend Sarah Hatoff does.

She Gave us the info.

And speaking of Sarah...

...We HAVE A BiG SuRPrISE!

But we can't tell You until

SARAH iS COMiNG TOMORROW!!!

HEY! That was supposed to be a SURPRISE!!!

Sowwy!

ARE WE GONNA BE on TV?

Yeah, probably!

And I expect you children to be on your BEST BEHAVIOR!!!

Aw, maaaan!!!

We're Gonna be **FAMOUS!!!**

Does Anyone want my autograph?

No.

NAOMI's the FAMOUS One!

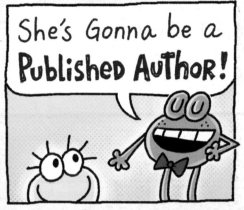

She's Gonna be a **Published Author!**

Psst! And illustrator!

AND ILLUSTRATOR!

CHAPTER 4
NAOMI'S REVELATION

I used to think that only **SOME** people could draw...

...and the rest of us were out of luck.

But then I **REALIZED**...

... I can write my **NAME!**

So what? We can all do **that!!!**

BUT– Are You **WRITING** Your names...

Naomi

...or are you **DRAWING** Your names?

Naomi the Great

Every letter and number you can think of...

...is just a buncha lines, dots, circles, and curves.

Every **DRAWING** is the same, too!

They're all just a buncha lines, dots, circles, and curves!

The only reason we can **DRAW** our names...

...is because we've **PRACTICED!!!**

Now, draw a biG letter "M" on top.

Add two periods...

...and a little baby "O" underneath.

Now, make a **BiG** capital "D"...

...but make it **SiDEWAYS**...

...and put two little upside-down "U"s right here.

Now color in the capital "D"...

...except for the "U" parts.

WOW! HEY! We're DRAWING! WE RULE!

The arms and legs are easy!

You just draw a sideways "C"...

54

...and then draw another one right next to it.

Hey! This is **EASY!**

Yeah!

But what about hands?

Yeah! Hands are **HARD!**

No they're not!

Just draw a baby "C"...

...then draw **one**...

...**Two**...

...**Three** more!

The feet are even **EASIER!**

Just draw a sideways "J."

COOOOOL!!!

Now, the tail **SEEMS** hard...

...but it's just a curved "V"...

... with a "W" at the end.

And for fur, just draw a buncha little baby lines.

Hey! My werewolf is **NAKED!!!**

DADDY! Naomi's making me draw **FULL-FRONTAL NUDITY!!!**

HA! HA! HA! HA! HA! HA! HA! HA! HA! HA! HA! HA! HA!

Alright, alright...

HA! HA! HA! HA! HA! HA! HA! HA!

...Who can tell me the lesson You just learned?

I just learned something, Daddy!

What is it, Starla?

Well, I didn't think I could draw...

...but look! I can **TOTALLY** draw!!!

I just hadn't **PRACTICED!**

I'll bet if I **PRACTICE** a whole bunch...

... I'll be able to do **ANYTHING!**

Yeah!

Makes sense to me!

And so...

Naomi!

Yes, Daddy?

You did a **VERY GOOD** job teaching everyone today!!!

Thanks!

I've been trying to teach you kids that lesson **ALL YEAR...**

CHAPTER 5

SHE WRITES BACK

63

And **DON'T FORGET:**

BEST BEHAVIOR!

Man, this hasn't even started yet...

...and I'm already **BORED!**

And
So...

...but
then...

Y'all Got Mail!

Welcome,
Ms.
Hatoff

Hey! Daddy forgot his Phone!!!

Melvin, we're supposed to stay in our **Seats!**

I'm tellin'!!!

Let Me See! Let Me See!

You GuYs aren't Supposed to play With DaddY's phone!

WE'RE NOT PLAYING!

This is Business!

Look! She wrote mY Name! "Melvin T. FroG."

She wrote MY Name, too!!! "Naomi T. Great."

'Global sameness' fails to recognize that everybody isn't always given the same opportunities or chances in life. Furthermore, some lines in the story (i.e. 'just poke your nose beneath your clothes, you'll see we're all the same'), could be seen as making controversial statements about gender that may offend or diminish many readers."

Just skip to the end!

NO! I'm READING!

You read too slow!

Give it to me! NO!!!

Let Go! Give it!!!

73

Wait. Does this mean we're not Getting our ice-cream machine?

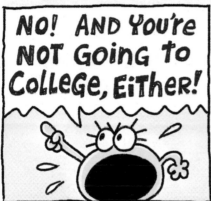

NO! AND You're NOT Going to College, Either!

I WAS Supposed To PAY FOR *THAT*, Too, Apparently!

NO ICE CREAM?

BUT I LOVE ICE CREAM!

IT'S ALL I've EVER WANTED!

Meanwhile...

We're so happy you're here, Sarah.

Thanks, FLippy! I'm excited to meet the **COMiC CLUB!**

Well, I think You'll be delighted by my kids!

They're so **CREATiVE...**

... so **MATURE...**

... and always on their **BEST BEHAViOR!!!**

CHAPTER 6
OUR WORST BEHAVIOR

WHAT ON EARTH is GOING ON???

Naomi said we can't have an ice-cream machine!

AND we have to Go to College!

NO! We CAN'T Go to college!

Oh.

AND we CAN'T GO TO COLLEGE!!!

SLap!

...So then Melvin and Naomi Got into a **FiGht**...

...**AND** they broke Your **Phone**...

I told them not to!

...And now they're embroiled in a bitter Breach-of-contract dispute!!!

I swear, I was Just Gone for **Five Minutes!!!**

FlippY?

This is...

...AWESOME!!!

Wait, what?

I thought this WAS Just Gonna be a **CUTE, LiTTLE STORY!**

Just two minutes of "feel-Good" FLuff!

But this STORY has **PASSiON...**

...DRAMA...

Clear my **ENTIRE** Schedule, Roscoe!

Okay, Sarah!

We're Gonna do some **IN-DEPTH REPORTING!**

Got it!

And Get Ready, Kids...

...because You're **ALL** Gonna be **FAMOUS!**

HOORAY!!!

CHAPTER 7

SARAH HATOFF
SPECIAL REPORT

COMIC CENSORSHIP
THE EMERGENCY ALERT
THAT COULD SAVE YOUR FREEDOM

KEEPING OUR CHILDREN SAFE

BREAKING NEWS WITH SARAH HATOFF

... COMIC CLUB CHAOS: THE AFTERMATH... PROPERTY DESTROYED... LONGTIME MEMBER QUITS IN HEART-BREAKING

'Sup? I'm Sarah Hatoff...

...and welcome to my Special Report.

The Cat Kid Comic Club is now in its **Third week**...

...and **TENSIONS** are **SKY-HiGH!!!**

Tell me: Has the recent tension affected you?

HOW has it affected you?

My sister got mad and quit...

...and now I have to sit all by myself.

Why don't you just move over?

I CAN'T sit in **HER** SEAT!

Oh, dear! This kid needs some **CHEERING UP!!!**

But how can we help him?

I know!!!

What?

We can read our new comic to him!!!

SUPA FAIL 3

Let's Do it!

93

95

98

100

It was the same thing over and over...

...and then it just **ENDED!!!**

Where's the **PLOT** and the **CHARACTER development?**

Yeah! And how come Supa Fail has **SUPERPOWERS?**

He didn't have them in the **FIRST** book!

Yeah!

You never **explained** it!

CHAPTER 8

The Time Out Rock

Okay, I told 'em!

Time out.

Time Out.

Time Out.

I WANNA be LEFT ALONE, POPPY!!!

Yeah, me too!

PLOP!

Everyone misses you!

 Well I'm **NOT COMING BACK!!!**

 OKay...

 ...but why?

 IT'S Embarrassing!

 All I did was try to **DO GOOD**...

 ... And I ended up **OFFENDING EVERYBODY!!!**

Wait. Who Got offended?

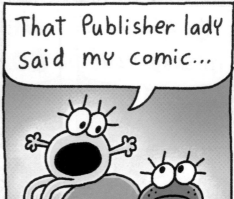

That Publisher lady said my comic...

...made statements about **GENDER** that are **OFFENSIVE!!!!!!!!**

Out.

Wendy and EL probably **HATE** me now!!!

No they don't.

They were just looking for you!

They were so **WORRieD!!!**

Really? Yeah!

I should probably go talk to them.

Hey, Naomi...

...Poppy said **SHHH!**

whisper whisper whisper...

Oh Yeah. We Got an **Anonymous** tip...

...that You wanted to talk to Us.

YYYeah. I did.

115

Remember those parts where I said...

... Something like...

.."everybody's the same underneath"?

Yeah.

Kind of.

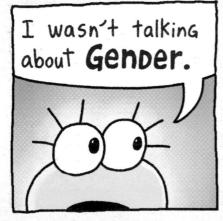

I wasn't talking about **Gender.**

Yeah. We know.

CHAPTER 10

NEW DAY, NEW COMICS

Well, it's a **NEW DAY...**

...and it's time for some ALL-NEW COMICS!

Who wants to Go **First?**

We Do! We Do!

We made this comic with cardboard and clay and stuff...

...and it's called:

Space: A froGGY frontier.

These are the VOYAGes of the BaBY FroG SQUAD.

Our Mission: To seek out space Bullies...

...And send 'em packin'.

Deep inside the Sleeping Deck...

Our heroes Frankie, C.C., and Boo are dreaming of Justice...

... While I, their trusted navigator...

...Set a course for adventure...

...to boldly Jump where no froG has Jumped before.

Suddenly...

We're heading to Planet #61.

'Sup, Brutus?

It's another danGerous mission, I'm afraid.

Well **We're** NOT!!!

Let's Go, SQUAD!!!

But then...

HeY!!!

What happened to our Space BuGGies?

I made some improvements while y'all were asleep.

Thanks, Buddy! How can we ever repay you?

How about a hug?

OKay!!!

Aren't you gonna give Brutus a hug?

I'm not really a hugger.

Thanks, Baby Frog Squad!

No Prob!!!

Now all I have to do is drive around...

...and around...

...aGain and aGain...

...and aGain and aGain!!!

I Guess that **WRAPS UP** our story!!!

HA HA HA HA HA HA HA HA

HA HA HA HA HA HA HA

But then...

HiYA, FroGGies!

Oh, hi, Brutus.

What's up?

Nothing. We're Just flying to our deaths.

Oh.

Well, can I tell Y'all something **NOW??**

... Just press the new "Transform" button I made...

... and it'll be **PARTY TIME!**

Gee, thanks, pal!

We'll Give that a try!!!

Hmmm...

141

Well, I don't know about you two...

...but when I Get back to the ship...

TO BE CONTINUED

Credits:

Story by: Billie
art by: Frida and EL and Deb
photography and editing by: Billie and EL

That was **WONDERFUL!!!**

Thanks!

thanks!

thanks!

thanks!

Who made those Colorful Robots?

Me and Deb and Frida!

We used salad dressing lids and wire and clay...

... and tape dispensers for their feet!!!

146

Everyone was worried...

...because Ghost Girl was so sad.

She missed her old cat very much...

...And everything she did...

...made her feel sadder...

...and sadder.

Let's all play Skelopup's new Game.

Here are the rules:

For 30 minutes...

...We must all be happy.

But what if we **CAN'T** be happy?

Then we'll **PRETEND!!!**

...so she sat up straight and tall...

...and smiled a BIG pretend smile, too.

This FEELS DUMB!!!

But it felt kind of nice, too.

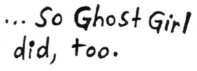

Skelopup and Skeleton Boy jumped and ran...

...So Ghost Girl did, too.

This feels strange!!!

But it felt kind of nice, too.

Skelopup and Skeleton Boy laughed BIG Pretend Laughs!

So Ghost Girl did, too.

HA HA HA HA HA HA

This feels silly!

HA HA HA HA

But it felt kind of nice, too.

...HEY! these are the Pictures that make me sad.

Ghost Girl looked up at the clock tower.

She knew she could be sad again soon...

So for now, she tried to find a way...

...to make her sad Photos feel happy.

Even though my Old cat is gone...

...and I'll never see him again...

...I'm happy that he was here for a while...

...and that I Got to be his friend.

...So they slept and slept and slept.

THE END

ABout the Author/Illustrator:

POPPY

Poppy Likes to draw and ~~tell~~ make up Ghost stories and think about stuff. She hopes we can still Get a ice cream machine even though she is Lactose intolerant because it will be worth it if everybody else can be happy. Maybe it can make sorbet, too, which is good if you get used to it. But not Lemon which is gross.

WOW! That was LOVELY!!!

Thanks, Sarah!

Oops. I mean, "Thanks, Ms. Hatoff!"

Oh, please. Call me "Sarah."

Okay, Sarah!

So Melvin, did Poppy's comic cheer you up?

Well, Sarah...

...To be perfectly honest, Sarah...

Ummm... it **DID** cheer me up...

...But it Also Gave me an **AWESOME IDEA**...

...Ms. Hatoff.

CHAPTER 11

Melvin's Awesome Idea

166

I'm just scanning these comics.

Why?

Because they're gonna be **PUBLISHED!**

Will you email them to that Publisher lady for me???

Melvin, haven't you learned your **Lesson?**

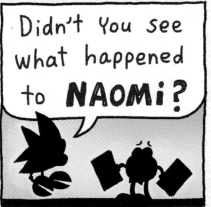

Didn't you see what happened to **NAOMI?**

That **Rejection** broke her heart...

...and now she's **Quit** the **Club!**

Do you really want to Go through all of that **AGAIN???**

No... but...

...I **CAN'T** Give up!

You Always tell us to Keep trYinG...

...even if thinGs Get hard.

You alwaYs saY...

..."**FAiLure** is a **STeppinG-STOne** to **SUCCess!**"

RiGht, DaddY???

Yeah. I **DO** saY that a lot.

Great! Then it's all settled!

Let me know when that Publisher lady writes back, okay?

But...

Okay...

CHAPTER 12

New Comic, Old Problem

Welcome back to a new day of thrills and drama!

What can you tell us about your new comic?

Well, it's, ummm...

...Uh...

...we made it, umm...

...it's like...

...uhh...

Just read the comic.

Okay!

CHUBBS McSPIDERBUTT

PART 2: The Birth of Big Bubba Babyhead

WRITTEN AND DIRECTED BY **THE HACKER BROS.**

When we last Saw our heroes...

...They were being terribly tormented...

...by the Not Very Nice Club!!!

Your Daddy has training wheels on his tricycle!

Yeah! And I'll bet he's really **SMART**, too!!!

176

I know! And our mean insults didn't bother them, either!

What we need is some **MUSCLE!**

Come on, Scott!!!

Let's turn this van around!!!

I know **JUST** the guy who can help us!!!

SHOOOMM!

Soon, they arrived at the home of BiG Bubba Boxerbuns.

What do **YOU** want?

I invite You to **Join US!!!**

ToGether we shall defeat Chubbs McSpiderbutt!!!

I GoT No beef With Chubbs!!!

Oh, reallY?

Well he said Your Gym shorts and dress shoes look silly together.

No he didn't!

Shhh!

Oh, he **Did,** did he?

So Chubbs McSpiderbutt thinks he can insult MY Fashion Sense...

...and Get AWAY with it ?????

CHUBBS iS Goin' Down!

Meanwhile...

Mmm! This sushi is GOOD!!!

Are you gonna eat your uni?

It's all yours, Little buddy!

Thanks!

Hey Jake, do you think we will ever be **FAMOUS?**

You mean like Spider-Man?

No Parent is Going to buy Their kid a SPider-Man T-Shirt...

...if he's shooting a buncha webs...

...OUT OF his BUTT!!!

That's DISGUSTING!!!

THAT'S FAKE Science!

AH-CHOOOOO!!!

Well, Chubbs...

... We may be famous someday...

...but I don't think we'll sell too many T-shirts!!!

Meanwhile...

CHUBBS McSPIDERBUTT...

COME OUT and PLAY-YAY!!!!

WARNING: Low-Hanging Sign

CHUBBS?

Gee, I wonder where he could be?

WARNING: Low-Hanging Sign

And so...

THANKS A LOT, SCOTT!

KA-CLICK

You RAN OVER MY HEAD!

I CAN'T GO AROUND LOOKING LIKE THIS!

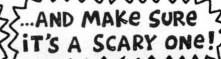

GO BUY ME A NEW HEAD!!!

...AND MAKE SURE IT'S A SCARY ONE!

OKAY!

Here I Go!!!

Dum-dee-dum-dee dumm...

This must be the Place!!!

HEADS "R" US

And So...

La-dee-da-duhhh...

What took You So LonG ???

GiMMe That!

HEY!!!

WiLL the Not Very Nice CLub **FinALLY** Defeat Chubbs & Jake?

WiLL our heroes ever appear on officially Licensed T-shirts?

WiLL Scott overcome his fear of babies?

Find out in the next thrilling Adventure of

CHUBBS McSPiDeRBuTT

That was very Good, Drake!!!

Thanks!

Me and Gilbert and Rico made it **TOGETHER!**

Hey, Melvin! You should send our book to that **Publisher LADY!!!**

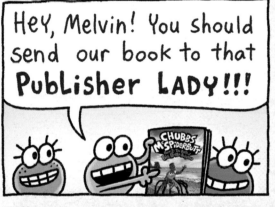

CHUBBS McSPIDERBUTT

ARE YOU Kidding?

THAT COMIC WAS VERY OFFENSIVE!

It's All About BUTTS!!!

Nobody is ever Gonna buy a book with **BUTT JOKES** in it!

Besides...

That Publisher lady takes **FOREVER** to write back!!!

She Probably won't write back until **NEXT YEAR!!!**

Y'all Got Mail

Melvin? She wrote back.

196

CHAPTER 13

Just be You

And So... ...Then she said my comic was **DISTURBING...**

...which means that **I'm Disturbing!**

That's **NOT** what it means, POPPY.

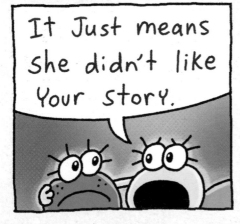

It Just means she didn't like Your story.

She didn't like **MINE,** either!

But a very wise person once said...

Everybody doesn't have to like the same things.

And I'm **GLAD** they don't!

Do you want to live in a world...

...where everybody is the same?

NO WAY!

THAT would be **DISTURBING!**

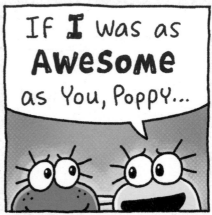

If **I** was as **AWESOME** as You, PoppY...

...I wouldn't change a **ThinG!**

OkaY, I won't!

See Ya Later!!!

Oh, hi, DaddY!

Time Out.

Hi, PoppY.

Hi, Naomi.

Hey!

Are you ready to rejoin the club?

I guess so.

I overheard what you said to Poppy back there.

Those were very wise words.

Yeah, I know.

You're good at **COMFORTING** people!

Hey!!!

Maybe you've found your **PURPOSE!!!**

Maybe you're going to be a **COUNSELOR** someday!!!

Do counselors make a lot of money?

Well, not usually, but the **PASS!**

206

CHAPTER 14

A Buncha Stuff That Changed Everything

Soon...

Guess what? I'm **BACK!!!**

Are you going to change your comic?

nope!

I'm just gonna be **Me!**

Hey, everyone!

Look who **ELSE** is Back!!!

209

No, Pedro. We can't—

Y'all Got Mail

Melvin— She wrote bAck aGain!!!

NO THANKS!

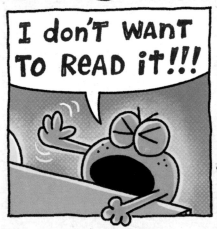

I don'T WANT TO REAd it!!!

It's about BABy FroG SQUAD!

Oh, GREAT!

ALL YOU have to do is make **TWO HUNDRED MORE PAGES**, And—

Wait, what?

It has to be **224** Pages!!!

224 PAGES?

We Can't Make 224 PAGES!!

THAT'S WAY TOO MANY PAGES!!!

Go on, Get in there!

Pat Pat Pat

I **LOVE** being a Director, Daddy!

It's the **Perfect** Job for me!!!

I'm Good at **STOrytelling**...

...I'm Good at **Bossing People Around**...

Well, folks, we've come to the end of a **DRAMATIC** DAY!

WILL everyone be able to **WORK TOGETHER?**

WILL Naomi's **CRAVING** for **CASH** be her **DOWNFALL?**

And **WILL** the **BABY** FROGS **EVER STAY** in BED?

FIND OUT IN OUR NEXT THRILLING ADVENTURE!!!

CAT KID COMIC CLUB

BOOK 4 is COMING SOON!

NOTES & FUN FACTS

☆ The cover artwork for this book was made from cardboard, wire, crumpled-up construction paper, putty, acrylic paints, glue, and a small sheet of fake grass.

☆ Most of the planets in BABY FROG SQUAD are balloons, airbrushed with markers, that were photographed in front of a light bulb. The planet that looks like a melon is a close-up photo of the plastic lid of a fruit cup.

☆ The Baby Frog Squad's bunk beds were made out of matchboxes glued to bamboo shish-kebab skewers.

☆ Over 2,000 photographs were taken for the Chubbs McSpiderbutt mini comic, but only 111 were used.

☆ Chubbs is correct on page 182. Spiders DO produce webs from their spinnerets, located at the tips of their abdomens (their butts). Most spiders don't "shoot" webs, but a few do. The Darwin's bark spider can "shoot" a web up to 82 feet (25 meters) long. Sweeeet!!!

☆ Big Bubba Babyhead's gym shorts came from a 1972 action figure called "Big Jim." This action figure also inspired a character in the Dog Man series.

☆ The Ethel Merman Disco Album really DOES exist, although it is rarely used to frighten baby frogs.

☆ Melvin's words on page 169 were inspired by the following Quote:

"Discouragement and failure are two of the surest stepping-stones to Success."

— Dale Carnegie

KEEP READING WITH DAV PILKEY!

Go to planetpilkey.com to read chapters, make comics, watch videos, play games, and download supa fun stuff!

The epic musical adventure is now available from Broadway Records!

ABOUT THE
AUTHOR-ILLUSTRATOR

When Dav Pilkey was a kid, he was diagnosed with ADHD and dyslexia. Dav was so disruptive in class that his teachers made him sit out in the hallway every day. Luckily, Dav loved to draw and make up stories. He spent his time in the hallway creating his own original comic books — the very first adventures of Dog Man and Captain Underpants.

In college, Dav met a teacher who encouraged him to write and illustrate for kids. He took her advice and created his first book, WORLD WAR WON, which won a national competition in 1986. Dav made many other books before being awarded the California Young Reader Medal for DOG BREATH (1994) and the Caldecott Honor for THE PAPERBOY (1996).

In 2002, Dav published his first full-length graphic novel for kids, called THE ADVENTURES OF SUPER DIAPER BABY. It was both a USA Today and New York Times bestseller. Since then, he has published more than a dozen full-length graphic novels for kids, including the bestselling Dog Man and Cat Kid Comic Club series.

Dav's stories are semi-autobiographical and explore universal themes that celebrate friendship, empathy, and the triumph of the good-hearted.

When he is not making books for kids, Dav loves to kayak with his wife in the Pacific Northwest.

Learn more at Pilkey.com.